# THE WIDOW'S BURDEN

## BY ROBERT COOPERMAN

WESTERN REFLECTIONS PUBLISHING COMPANY

Montrose, CO

"And they are gone: aye, ages long ago
Those lovers fled away into the storm."
—John Keats, *The Eve of St. Agnes*

I would like to thank Rich Yurman and Charles
Rammelkamp, once again, for their sensitive and perceptive
reading of the manuscript and for their insightful remarks
and comments.

For Jeff and Lori, for Bill and Diane;

and as always, for Beth:
until the rivers run dry and the mountains turn to dust

∾

Copyright © 2002 Robert Cooperman
All rights reserved including the right of reproduction in
whole or in part.

First Edition
Printed in the United States of America

ISBN 1-890437-63-8

Illustrations by Michael Welply
Cover and text design by Laurie Goralka Design

Western Reflections Publishing Company
P.O. Box 1647
Montrose, CO 81402
www.westernreflectionspub.com

# Table of Contents

The Badman John Sprockett Explains His Chivalry to Women
and His Love of Books: Gold Creek, Colorado Territory, 1871 ....2
The Reverend Thomas Burden Considers His Calling ......................5
John Sprockett Recalls a Horrifying Incident from His Years
with Raiders in Bloody Kansas......................................................6
The Reverend Thomas Burden Thinks of Jesus ...............................8
Lavinia Burden Reflects on Why She Married the Reverend
Thomas Burden ............................................................................10
The Tracker William Eagle Feather Muses on His Name ...............11
Reverend Burden Compares Mary LaFrance with His Wife Lavinia....12
Reverend Burden Contemplates Francis DeLacey, Publisher of the
Gold Creek Optimist....................................................................14
Reverend Burden Comes to a Fateful Decision...............................16
Reverend Burden Speaks Privately with John Sprockett.................18
John Sprockett, After His Murder of Reverend Burden ..................21
Shorty Cameron Witnesses the Reverend Burden's Last Moments ...22
Dying, the Reverend Burden Recalls Leading a Rescue Party .........24
Mary LaFrance, Annoyed That Preacher Burden Has Forgotten
Their Assignation..........................................................................26
Two Boys Make a Dreadful Discovery.............................................28
Olive Phalen, Formerly of New York: Laundress.............................30
Mary LaFrance Learns Why Reverend Burden Missed Their
Appointment .................................................................................32
Lavinia Burden, the Night Her Husband Died ...............................34
The Widow Burden, at the Funeral of Her Late Husband...............36
William Eagle Feather Attends the Funeral of the Reverend
Burden...........................................................................................38
Silver Hands Muldoon Plays Piano at the Funeral of the
Reverend Burden..........................................................................40
Francis DeLacey, Publisher of the Gold Creek Optimist, Eulogizes
the Late Reverend Burden ...........................................................42
John Sprockett, After the Funeral of Reverend Burden ..................44
Lawrence van Gelder, President of the Gold Creek Bank, After
the Funeral....................................................................................46
In the Wake of the Suspicious Death of Reverend Burden, Sheriff
Dennehy Calls in an Expert..........................................................48
Edgar Goodrich, After the Burial of Reverend Burden...................50

William Eagle Feather Fails To Divulge How Reverend Burden
  Died.................................................................................................52
Sheriff Dennehy Speculates on the Death of Reverend Burden......55
Mary LaFrance, After Her Talk with Sheriff Dennehy ....................56
The Diva Lucrezia Falcone Arrives in Gold Creek After the
  Death of Reverend Burden.............................................................58
Mary LaFrance Speculates on the Father of Her Unborn Child .....60
Sheriff Dennehy, After the Coroner's Inquest.................................62
Dr. O'Rourke Ponders the Badman John Sprockett and the Late
  Reverend Burden.............................................................................64
The Widow Burden, the Night After Her Husband's Funeral.........66
The Widow Burden, Three Nights After her
  Husband's Funeral..........................................................................68
William Eagle Feather Contemplates the Widow Burden ...............70
The Widow Burden's Suspicions About John Sprockett..................71
Mary LaFrance Ponders Her Relationship to the Late
  Reverend Burden.............................................................................72
The Widow Burden, After Her Second Interview with
  John Sprockett................................................................................74
John Sprockett, After His Second Interview with the
  Widow Burden................................................................................76
Sylvia Williams, Boarding House Owner .........................................78
Max Longstreet, Gambler, Speculates on the Death of
  Reverend Burden.............................................................................80
William Eagle Feather Gives Lavinia Burden a New Name............82
John Sprockett Considers the Widow Burden and William
  Eagle Feather ..................................................................................84
William Eagle Feather, After a Visit from Chief Many Horses........86
Sheriff Dennehy Makes His Intentions Plain to the
  Widow Burden................................................................................88
Lavinia Burden Replies to Sheriff Dennehy's Proposal
  of Marriage......................................................................................90
The Widow Burden, After Rejecting Sheriff Dennehy's Suit..........92
Sheriff Dennehy, After His Rebuffed Proposal.................................94
The Widow Burden, Caught in a Quandary.....................................96
William Eagle Feather, Impatient for an Answer.............................98
The Widow Burden Meets William Eagle Feather Outside of
  Gold Creek ...................................................................................100
Lavinia Burden Risks Everything...................................................102

William Eagle Feather Flees Gold Creek with the
    Widow Burden.............................................................................104
Sheriff Dennehy Discovers the Widow Burden Gone....................106
Mary LaFrance, After the Widow Burden's Escape.........................108
Madam Jezebel LeDoux, After the Widow Burden's Escape..........110
Brutus Hawkins, Bouncer, Speaks of the Widow Burden..............112
Sheriff Dennehy Recruits a Posse from Those Drinking in
    His Saloon...................................................................................114
Francis DeLacey Rides in the Posse After the Widow Burden
    and William Eagle Feather..........................................................116
Sheriff Dennehy, Once the Posse Returns.....................................118
John Sprockett, After the Posse Returns........................................121
Mary LaFrance Watches the Posse Return.....................................122
William Eagle Feather Hears of the Death of
    John Sprockett, 1876...................................................................124
William Eagle Feather Changes His Name.....................................126
Hair Filled With Sun: the Colorado Rockies, Late 19th Century....128
Finds the Path Mourns..................................................................130

∾

# Acknowledgements

The author is grateful to the editors of the journals listed below for
permission to reprint the following poems, some in an earlier form:

*Comstock Review,* "The Widow Burden, Caught in a Quandary"

*Cumberland Poetry Review,* "The Widow Burden, at the Funeral of
Her Late Husband"

*Ilya's Honey,* "Reverend Burden Contemplates Francis DeLacey,
Publisher of the Gold Creek Optimist"

*Main Street Rag,* "Mary LaFrance, After the Widow Burden's Escape"

*Now Here Nowhere,* "In the Wake of the Suspicious Death of
Reverend Burden, Sheriff Dennehy Calls in an Expert"

*The Amethyst Review,* "Shorty Cameron Witnesses the Reverend
Burden's Last Moments"

## The Badman John Sprockett Explains His Chivalry to Women and His Love of Books: Gold Creek, Colorado Territory, 1871

In her few free minutes,
Mama'd read me poems,
rhymes sweet as a sugar-tit.
The last time, me fifteen
and strong as railroad ties,
Pa spat she was Devil-spawn,
and laid into her
like a centurion with a whip,

shoved her into the table,
dinner crashing against the walls,
ripped her book's pages
like decks of blushing cards,
then threw it into the hearth,
Mama begging, "God loves beauty."

"Beauty's a sin!" he bellowed,
slapped her so hard she fell
like a galloping mount caught
by a gaping gopher hole.

That's when I hit him
with his Bible, heavy as an anvil:
hit him and hit him and hit him,
till he didn't move.

That night she was fever-took.
She breathed easier to hear me
recite poems like birdsong.
I'm thankful she passed peaceful,
the finest woman to walk this earth.

After I buried her,
left him for the hogs and buzzards,
I saddled his favorite horse
and rode off slow and mean.

❧

## The Reverend Thomas Burden
## Considers His Calling

As a boy I was called by the Lord
to cry out against all evil nesting
like cottonmouths in a river.
My sermons made grown men weep,
women screech and speak in tongues.
Everyone said I had the power
of the Lord in my voice and eyes.

Now, a viper stings my vitals,
but I can't tell Lavinia
that Mary LaFrance's white breasts
beckon like snow-capped peaks,
promising the sight of God
and all His dancing angels.

Mary longs for San Francisco,
but if we sneak off like Jonah —
swallowed by the whale
of his disobedience —
I'll end up blaming Mary
for my sliding into sin;
she'll grow bitter as Lavinia:
my barren wife spinning webs
of gall beside our unhappy hearth.

No, I'll see Mary when I can,
offer her my hand
if something befalls Lavinia,
though it's a sin even to hope
for her untimely, accidental death.

☙

## John Sprockett Recalls a Horrifying Incident from His Years with Raiders in Bloody Kansas

The farmhouse and barn burned
yellow as Hell-flames.
The farmer and his sons lay dead,
their women staked spread-eagle,
like we was marauding Apaches
and not proud Rebel raiders.

Colonel let the men take turns
on the mother and daughter;
their shrieks for mercy
cut me like broken whiskey bottles.

"Sprockett!" Quantrill spoke sharp
as a flywheel honing swords,
"you gonna try your luck,
or afraid even these two'll object
to your grizzly-ripped face?"

"Mister," the older one begged,
both their legs blood-smeared,
"if you ever loved your mama,
kill us quick." The other sobbed,
young enough to hope we'd let her live.

A bullet apiece,
and they were in Heaven
with Mama, praying for me,
I hope. That was the end
of my raiding days,
though I had to ride hard
to put miles between me
and the Colonel's balked pleasure.

❧

## The Reverend Thomas Burden Thinks of Jesus

I used to believe Him
too good-natured about whores,
before I was blessed
with knowing Miss Mary LaFrance.
Lavinia wouldn't understand
our affection; no need to tell her.
I can see her measuring my flock
of rough miners against her daddy's
congregation of Boston bigwigs;
believing themselves higher
than God and my rough preaching,
her wishing in her silent heart
to be back with her Daddy.

He's dead, her aunt wrote,
the old raven flying down to Hell
after him: couldn't wait
to take up with him in the next life,
his housekeeper in this one
after his wife died;
the two biddies'll cat-claw
each other's eyes out in Perdition.

I'm all Mary's got in this world,
and tell her Jesus is the road
to her salvation in the next.
The trusting child believes me
with eyes dewy as the pure dawn,
while Lavinia smiles at my sermons
as if she's holy as God's Mother:
her way of saying my testifying's
nothing but chimney smoke.

∽

## Lavinia Burden Reflects on Why She Married the Reverend Thomas Burden

Father — himself a minister
I would no more think of disobeying
than I would of running off with gypsies —
was awed by Reverend Burden's sermons:
celebrated in our Boston
as if Mr. Keane performing Othello.

I too was tranced by his magnetism.

Only Aunt — who raised me
after Mother perished pushing me
into this world — saw Mr. Burden
for an Italian poisoner of rich brides.

She tried every argument,
though we knew I had as little choice
against Father's wishes
as virgins sacrificed to Baal.
Her final, desperate effort:
"You obey your father only because
it galls him you aren't a son."

I've accompanied my husband
to the most sordid of the gold camps,
rescuing souls snared by the demon-ore.
His sermons flicker with holy flames,
but his eyes burn at the temptations
Satan heaps upon these mountains.

## The Tracker William Eagle Feather
## Muses on His Name

Spawned by a white trapper
sheltered for a night by a Ute woman
stolen by raiding Lakotas
and treated no better than a slave,
I was the boy mud was flung at
after Mother died,
coughing red blizzards.

My name: "William"
came to me after John Sprockett
recited a poem by that Shakespeare,
at a funeral, something about not
fearing the sun no more.
I couldn't cipher half the words,
but the sounds wove pictures pretty
as geese across the falling-leaf sky.

I figured William Shakespeare
had powerful magic, so took his name.

"Eagle Feather:"
Mother said one fluttered down
at my birth: only reason
the tribe didn't set me out to die.

The one time I glimpsed
Preacher's wife, I wanted
to whisper my name in her ear
over and over and over.

ॐ

### Reverend Burden Compares
### Mary LaFrance with His Wife Lavinia

My wife never presented me
with proof she's strong
in the Lord: a son.
Mary has, or will,
in five months' time:
more my lawful wife
in God's eyes
than church-Lavinia
ever was.

But I'm shackled to her,
a prisoner of war
who hates his cell-mate.

I'd sue for annulment,
Lavinia's desert-womb a sin.
But Mary and I'd have to quit
Gold Creek, parishioners
turning on me for tearing
that contract asunder.

I want to spend my days
here, beloved of my flock,
my son rising to my pulpit
when I lay down my burden
of leading sinners
to the Light.

If only I could find
some Bible precedent,
like the one about witches.

## Reverend Burden Contemplates Francis DeLacey, Publisher of the Gold Creek Optimist

A free and forthright press?
Nothing forthright
about the claws
that whiskey-breathed devil
sinks into me:
nosing out about Mary,
who I saved from whoredom;
set her up in a cottage
away from the weasel eyes
of them that spread gossip
like rancid honey
on moldy bread.

Mary needed a haven,
her bosoms heaving
penitence the first time
she offered me her jewel.
But that's between me and her:
my true wife in the Lord,
her ripening belly my altar.

But DeLacey's snouted us out;
I'll have to pay and pay,
to keep his tattling rag
from burning off the press
like the dirty hand of Satan
had set the type
and smeared the ink.
But I'll repay him,
no forgiveness for a bearer
of false witness.

Just as there's none
for Lavinia, barren as Egypt.

## Reverend Burden Comes to a Fateful Decision

I've asked the Lord
if it's necessary;
He's answered.
Still, it's dreadful
to think my wife must pay,
but a man of the Book
can't have the skunk whiff
of divorce clinging to him.

There's nothing for it
but to pay John Sprockett,
famous for the deaths
trailing him like cannon smoke.
He'll know how to do it clean,
fast, and merciful,
not like that soiled dove
we jerked years back.
She kicked and thrashed
like she was in the grip
of heathen lust.

Though it's not my hands
on Lavinia's throat,
not me tossing her down
the abandoned shaft
where I pay DeLacey,
to keep him quiet
about me and Mary,

still I tremble.

## Reverend Burden Speaks Privately
## with John Sprockett

I'm chief pillar
of the newly erected church
I had to bully from this town.
If I seek a divorce,
my flock'll be ravaged
like demons possessing swine.

What's one more murder to you,
wearing slaughtered souls as lightly
as savages decorate their belts
with Christian scalps?

My wife's no fit helpmate
for a man of God:
she fornicates with the Frenchman;
I've nosed out his letters to her,
destroyed them in a righteous frenzy.
She flaunts her adultery
like a biblical harlot.

When I confronted her,
she laughed the scorn
of Salome in my face,
rolled her hips
like Mistress Quickly:
you and me both love the Bard.

So here's my proposal:
a bag of purest dust, to toss
that strumpet into this dead shaft,
to avenge me like Othello.

∾

## John Sprockett, After His Murder
## of Reverend Burden

He thought me a simpleton,
quoting Shakespeare at me
like the Bard justified
the murder of a woman.
Then he accused his wife
and Emil the Frenchie:
as if she'd ever soil
her marriage vows.

I took the pouch he proffered
like mine were the dirtiest hands
his Bible-dainty fingers
had ever touched;
and since it was full dark
by the abandoned shaft
he wanted his wife to lie in,
I twisted his neck
quick as a chicken for the pot
when I was a Reb raider,
then flung him into the pit.

No one'll find him for a while.
The hard part's figuring out
how to sneak that pouch of dust
to his wife without her knowing
where it came from, or why.

❧

## Shorty Cameron Witnesses the
## Reverend Burden's Last Moments

One thing I've learned:
go against John Sprockett
and don't expect to live a minute.
When I spied him heaving
Preacher Burden into that mine,
like Moses smashing the Golden Calf
we're all coveting in these mountains,
I knew not to cry out.

Sprockett's a killer,
but unless he's mean-drunk
as the bear that raked his face,
he don't murder for no reason;
nor did I have any abiding respect
for that thundering Sunday hypocrite.
What Preacher Burden did
with Mary LaFrance wasn't Bible study.
Most likely they had a disagreement
about her, and it don't pay
to dispute John Sprockett over anything.

Preacher's wife always had a smile
for me, and a juicy slab of pie.
Her civilized conversation's
a welcome change from unbuttoning
my britches for whores
without even a how-dee-do.

I'd console her, but my claim's
more demanding than any wife.
Besides, if Sprockett figures out
who told her, my life'll be worth
less than a speck of pyrite.

∞

## Dying, the Reverend Burden Recalls
## Leading a Rescue Party

Oh, how I've fallen off!
Now, I lie broken for my sins;
once a good man. Ask Jack Manion,
who never failed to thank me
for saving his life, his soul.

Snow fell so satanically that year,
I feared to ring the Sabbath bell,
lest we'd be buried in drifts.
Between blizzards, a lone rider
gasped a tale of gold pilgrims
trapped on Perdition Pass.

I ordered a rescue party.
"They're dead, and we'll be too,"
Sheriff Dennehy gulped down whiskey:
my gaze determined as a hawk,
its wings catching the glory
of God's dawn.

Finally, we spotted five men.
As I helped Jack Manion down
the mountain — his toes frost-black
as rotted potatoes — he confessed
he'd shot a doomed soul
who'd drawn cannibal's short twig.
"He'll haunt me in Hell," he trembled.

"God forgives all," I assured.

He'll not forgive me, plotting
to have my inconvenient wife erased.

## Mary LaFrance, Annoyed That Preacher Burden Has Forgotten Their Assignation

Just like a man —
after he's huffed and puffed —
not to keep our appointment,
me with his mushroom in my belly.

First time he saw me,
he took my hands and whispered,
"The Lord has reserved a place
for thee among His elect."
That night, he snuck me
out of Miss Jezebel's,
whipped up his buggy
like Utes was chasing us,
hatchets in their blood-
bathed fists.

He toted me like a bride
into an abandoned shack,
did what even married men of God
do with irresistible whores,
then swore he wanted to marry me.

"You're already hitched," I reminded,
him grinding teeth like a wolf
gnawing its trapped paw
to free the rest of itself.

It's not like him to be late,
especially when he blessed my belly
and shouted, "Yes Jesus,
I will perform Thy dread will
upon my barren sinner of a wife!"

What he meant, I was afraid to ask.

## Two Boys Make a Dreadful Discovery

Me and Timmy double-dared
each other into that played-
out shaft, hoping
nuggets was lying around
like hardened horse turds.
That's when I stumbled over
something soft and scary.

I screeched
like my older sister clawed me
so fast I couldn't even think
of fighting that booger off.
When Timmy shined the lantern,
there was Preacher Burden,
dead as a donkey
a bear intends
to make leftovers out of.

We lit out of there
like all the banshees
in Ireland was chasing us:
me yelling for Timmy to stand
guard at the mine entrance,
whilst I fetched the Sheriff.

Saloon trash climbed
all over each other —
like wolves on winterkill —
so each could brag
he discovered the body.

∾

## Olive Phalen, Formerly of New York: Laundress

Da bartered me over and over,
men wild for a virgin —
or so he swore was my condition —
till I stole the cash he thought
himself clever as a Tammany boss
to hide under a floorboard.

When I landed on this gold mountain,
I got took under the broad black wings
of Preacher Burden's Sunday coat,
a good man — who cried my competence
with laundry and simple mending
to all and sundry —
though he's a damnation Baptist.

His wife too pure to dirty herself
cleaning his shirts;
I'd have married him,
if the job didn't mean
nastying the sheets at night.
How else, you'll ask, can we bring
good Catholics into this world?
Ask the Blessed Virgin.

Preacher Burden let me bide
in his house: my own bedroom
and a tin tub filled once a week
with hot water; lye soap
scouring the dirt off me.
He read to me from the Bible
till sleep washed me clean.

Wouldn't surprise me if his wife
shoved him down that dirty pit.

## Mary LaFrance Learns Why Reverend Burden Missed Their Appointment

Men've abandoned me
in every gold-cholera town
sweating its fever in these mountains,
but he's the first to fall
down an abandoned mine shaft.
Maybe he was escaping the baby
he'd stuffed inside me,
once it hit him his wife had him
in a grizzly death hug.

Or maybe he had help into the world
he was always preaching on
as if he'd seen Satan's caverns
and was reporting to the rest of us.

After my monthlies stopped,
he'd crow about the life inside me
like it was a mountain of gold.
I wanted us to run off together.
The funds he'd hid would set us up
till he could gather
a new congregation to toss nuggets
like we was sacred idols,
but he always said Gold Creek
was his home, his tabernacle.

Maybe he was finally fetching
that loot for our getaway,
and fell. I'd search it out,
but I'm heavy as that melon
I ate once, juice dripping
down my cheeks and fingers.
Lucky I never spent the presents
he was always laying at my feet.
I could sell some, and find a squaw
who knows how to get rid of
unwanted gifts from men who leave.

࿇

## Lavinia Burden, the Night Her Husband Died

I couldn't sleep, our bed
a listing ship, with Thomas away
at an important appointment.
With Mary LaFrance, of course;
but he thought me a simpleton.

Suddenly I heard a rustling.
"Thomas?" I called down.
Silence, terrible as a mountain
before it collapses on miners
drunk with stooping for gold.

When finally I grasped
the courage to investigate,
moonlight cast a beam onto a pouch
sitting mole-fat on my best table.
A shadow pressed against the wall:
John Sprockett, the most dangerous man
in the Territory. I trembled
to behold the side of his face
a grizzly had scarred jagged
as barbed wire's vicious slashes.

The pouch was as heavy with gold
as the skull of a buffalo;
then Mr. Sprockett vanished,
a shade returning to Hell.
I knew Thomas was dead,
felt, Christ forgive me, relief:
the hypocrite believing
God approved of his adulteries.

"Freedom," the gold whispered,
the face of that tracker
I'd talked to once
and was dazzled by his beauty,
shimmered for an instant,
as if in lake water.
I closed my eyes,
feared I'd see Thomas
the rest of my days.

☙

## The Widow Burden, at the Funeral
## of Her Late Husband

His whole congregation stares
as if I'd murdered him:
my guilt for secretly longing
for William Eagle Feather.
"A half-breed," Christians sneer.

Once, rambling on the mountain,
I came upon him, preparing
to spit a recently killed rabbit.
"Best for a woman not to travel
alone up here," he warned,
then invited me to partake.

I found myself licking my fingers
to prolong each delicious morsel,
then reluctantly returned to town,
accompanied part-way by William,
who left me within sight
of our church steeple.

Still pure, at least in body,
I rushed to prepare Thomas' dinner.

Now, innocent mourners silently
demand the run-off of my grief.
I oblige, having to live in this town,
too much to expect that William
will even guess I need rescuing.

# William Eagle Feather Attends the Funeral
## of the Reverend Burden

Not out of respect
for that demon crow-coat
that would cry, "Jesus!"
like he loaned Him
his best collar
and wanted it back,

but to catch a glimpse
of Preacher's widow:
her sun-colored hair,
features honest
as mountain flowers,
her hands that never
pluck nervous as spiders,
but lie in her lap,
calm as the moon.

Even from the back row
the Widow's tall and trim
as a lone pine
against the wind and rain.
her eyes settle on me
for an instant, lips upturned
quick as the flick
of a hummingbird's wings.

No, just a fancy:
the time she sat by my fire,
plain she thought me
an ignorant savage
unable to say
two smart words
to an Eastern lady.

❧

## Silver Hands Muldoon Plays Piano at the Funeral of the Reverend Burden

Congregation was scandalized
to sit in Miss Jezzy's brothel,
us with the town's one piano.
She charged them for my playing,
parishioners taking a collection,
less at the bank than expected,
but not polite to accuse
a dead preacher of theft,
though I knew him for a rascal
under his black Jesus-suit.

They wept while I played;
then Sprockett recited Scripture
and some fitting poems.
Mary took it harder than his widow,
who had to know of
his "Redemption Sessions,"
even if the rest of his flock
was innocent as sheared lambs.

Still, he had an angel side:
rescued Manion's party winter of '68.
Preacher never grabbed the credit,
a man to crow up his own holiness.

Like most, he was part angel, part devil.
Damn if I know which half won in the end.

## Francis DeLacey, Publisher of the Gold Creek Optimist, Eulogizes the Late Reverend Burden

"Dear friends,
we have gathered
to remember a saint
who made us richer
with the generosity
of his spirit,

"who'd want us
to rise
from the ashes
of our grief
and live wealthy
in his remembrance.

"Before he came to us,
we were swine rooting
for the yellow toadstools
we mistook
for sustenance.

"He threw ropes
of redemption
to us all,
teaching God's gold
is the true treasure.
He lifted fallen women
from their fleshly wallows,
and gave the currency
of Heaven to men
who stretched out hands
in direst need.

"Oh, we shall miss
this marvelous man
of God. Amen!"

## John Sprockett, After the Funeral
## of Reverend Burden

When Undertaker Stone asked me
to preside — no one but me left
within a hundred miles to spout
Scripture and Shakespeare by heart —
I almost confessed I killed that snake.
Any hesitation'd set Stone sniffing
like a slave-catcher's hound,
and I'd have to kill him too.

At graveside, I quoted Psalms 23
and 91, stampeded into the Bard's
"Fear No More the Heat O' the Sun,"
with its "Renowned be thy grave."
If his sobbing congregation knew
about his murdering fornicating ways,
they'd have kicked his dirty carcass
back down the same gold chute
where I'd flung that puffed-up spider.

I ended with one of my own poems.
It took two Chinese and me
all morning to dig his grave,
so I figured I was owed that vanity.
Afterwards, his widow clasped my paws,
like she knew what I'd done for her.

## Lawrence van Gelder, President of the Gold Creek Bank, After the Funeral

I'm the bearer of bad tidings
for his widow, their account not
nearly as flush as she might hope.
Preacher sipped at it
like a hip flask of brandy,
to satisfy Mary's expensive tastes.

I was besotted with the dove, too,
possessing a grace of form and face,
a generosity to laugh at bad jokes,
a cunning of fingers brushing
against trousers almost by accident.
She knows nothing moves a man
to gratitude like the advance,
retreat, advance of his pleasure.

When I tell Widow Burden,
she won't pitch a fantod,
as would Judge Sam's wife,
were she to learn His Honor moves funds
like a man cheating at checkers.
Miz Lavinia will stand sentry-smart,
and angular, only the set of her shoulders
hinting she could blow up the town
with her rage at Preacher's betrayal.

Maybe, heavy with sin, he plunged
down that played-out shaft.
Or someone envied his exclusive
enjoyment of Mary's talents:
Judge Delaney, for instance, a coward
who'd pay for his dirty business
to be taken care of by a third party.

∾

# In the Wake of the Suspicious Death of Reverend Burden, Sheriff Dennehy Calls in an Expert

I had a deputy fetch
that William Eagle Feather,
a better tracker than hounds
spooking a runaway slave from cover.
If anyone could find sign,
it was that half-blood,
his face giving nothing away,
like the time I complimented him,
"For a breed, you're a decent man."

After he scouted the mine entrance
Preacher fell, or was pushed, into —
sniffing, flicking through shrubs,
running eyes and hands over rocks
like they were bolts of fabric —
he slapped palms and muttered,
"Nothing."

Then he strode off to wherever
he camps when he don't fancy work.
I was hoping he'd point the finger
at John Sprockett, a murderer
who never rides into my town without
another cross going up in Boot Hill.

Maybe Undertaker Stone
appreciates Sprockett's handiwork,
but I shudder to think if him
and Eagle Feather ever partnered,
the one blasting half the Territory,
the other covering their tracks
like an evil magician.

∾

## Edgar Goodrich, After the Burial of Reverend Burden

His widow's too Eastern-prissy
to make friends with the wives
of us respectable merchants
trying to turn this slag heap
of gold-barking murderers
into a city fit for Christians.

Not that she walks around
giving instructions to angels;
but she lets it be known
her father was a Boston minister
holier than Jesus.

You ask me, that half-breed
William Eagle Feather
knows more than he'll tell
about the Preacher's death.
That boy's too good a tracker
not to read prints in ground
he swore was hard as a railroad tie;
blank as Pinhead Jones's head.

Widow Burden was seen
talking to him.
When it comes to pagans,
The Good Book says they'll burn;
so why engage them
in pleasant conversation,
if they're all going to Hell?

You ask me, it was more
than innocent palaver.

## William Eagle Feather Fails To Divulge
## How Reverend Burden Died

I'd never tell that fat
white slug of a sheriff —
him tossing me a coin
for my tracking jobs
like I'm a gold-tramp begging
free drinks in his saloon —

But from the faint boot marks,
it was John Sprockett flung
Preacher down the shaft.
Only thing I can't figure:
why that rhyme-crazy killer did it;
maybe he thought Preacher
wanted him run out of town.
Or it had to do with Preacher's wife.

I can read ground like Scripture:
Preacher was taken unsuspecting,
like a cougar had pounced on his bed.

The time I met his sweet widow
rambling on the mountain,
my heart did a courtship dance
so wild I could hardly speak.
Now, just let me find
some pretty words to say to her.

Sprockett owes me,
but I'm too frightened of him
to ask for a poem or two.

❧

## Sheriff Dennehy Speculates on the Death of Reverend Burden

If he was filled with lead,
especially a perforated spine,
I'd say the culprit
was that escapee from Hell,
John Sprockett, scars slashing
his face like someone smashed him
with a bottle of rotgut.

It looks like an accident;
but why would a man of God loiter
at that abandoned mine shaft?

We didn't smell no whiskey on him —
Preacher famous for temperance in a town
oiled by liquor and its gold river.
But rumors flew raucous as crows
about him and Mary LaFrance.
Wouldn't surprise me:
she can bewitch Jesus himself.

So her and me'll have a nice chat
if she wants to keep the company
of gold fever boys in my town.

Sprockett could've killed Preacher,
though why I can't cipher at all.
Still, when John spouts the Bard
like a flash flood, he can murder
anyone discourteous enough
not to listen. Maybe Preacher
didn't pay proper attention.

❧

## Mary LaFrance, After Her Talk
## with Sheriff Dennehy

When Sheriff tried to accuse me
of murdering Tommy, I jammed
my fists into my hips
that flare like rose petals,
and demanded, "Why would I want
to kill the golden goose
that was going to marry me
once he divorced his wife,
and call the baby I'm carrying his?"

Right then,
I knew our interview wouldn't end
till I gave proof of my innocence.
When he finished, we had an agreement:
I lie still for him now and again,
and he don't run me out of town
if folks blab about me and Tommy:
Dennehy not wanting
the Preacher's widow to smell
another woman on his corpse,
to sadden her already sorry heart.

Plain as her face,
Sheriff's sweet on her.

If she'd been more obliging,
Tommy'd never come to me.
Besides, everyone just pretends
he was straight as St. Peter,
when the only thing about him
not crooked was his root,
ripe as a stalk of sweet corn.

## The Diva Lucrezia Falcone Arrives in Gold Creek After the Death of Reverend Burden

When last I deigned
to perform for oafs and sluts
among the peaks my voice dwarfs,
*Pastore* Burden admonished
his congregation that to listen
to me was a sin greater than murder.
So I shed no tears for the vile man.

That time, a woman was hanged
for killing the man who beat her.
I commissioned a tragic opera
based on her life story,
even badmen sobbing at her fate.
Now, I return to perform
*The Death of Angelica,*
her real name prosaic as pyrite;
her looks enough to give pause
to even Hugo's bell-ringer:
myself an angel of passion,
William Cody once
my golden-haired seraph.

My manager maneuvers my return
to the opera houses of Europe,
to avenge myself on those singers
whose careers hoarsely soared
in the beds of impresarios,
my voice purer than a choirful
of Viennese castrati.

I'll commission a new opera:
*Pastore* Burden stabbed by his wife
for his many infidelities;
she'll turn the blade on herself —
existence unbearable without
her demon preacher.

How opera improves on life!

&

## Mary LaFrance Speculates on the Father of Her Unborn Child

I never told Preacher
it might not be his: no sense
stepping on a sunning rattler.
Sure, the Reverend set me up
in a cottage; but waiting
for his visits was long
as a moaning blizzard winter,
and Patience cards never turned up
my way, even when I cheated.
So I entertained, gifts handy,
had Preacher gone back on his word:
no telling how a white man'll act
when a baby bears him less
likeness than a papoose.

One man not in the contest,
One-eyed John Sprockett;
his grizzly-slashed face shudders me
like every ghost killed in the War.
Only other gent who can't join the list,
the breed tracker, Eagle Feather.
I only do white men, though I'd bet
Widow Burden wouldn't mind
a buggy ride to Heaven with him,
the way she stared at the funeral,
then shifted her eyes quick
as the flutter of a butterfly's wings.

Come to think of it,
I might make an exception for him,
his face more handsome
than the one of Jesus
I cut out of a book once,
to stare at on my wall.

## Sheriff Dennehy, After the Coroner's Inquest

If it'd been a gold rat
gunned down over a claim,
or a whore beaten to death
for not giving fair trade,
we could just shrug.
But this was Preacher Burden,
so we had to do something.

Doc O'Rourke testified
there wasn't no struggle;
the breed tracker swore
to no incriminating prints.

I wouldn't rule him out,
with folks feisty as weasels
in a small cage: a hanging
distracting as Miz Lucrezia,
who's more talented
in her dressing room
than when she's screeching
about princes and slaves,
what we fought two wars over.

But she's a welcome change
from the China doll I bought,
who cries whenever I poke her.

"Natural causes," we declared,
but what was Reverend doing
at that abandoned shaft
except to meet Mary LaFrance,
who maybe didn't fancy sharing
the church funds he sipped at,
like a thieving hummingbird?

But I couldn't bring that up,
not with Widow Burden up front,
her veil grieving her face
I've admired from the moment
she stepped off the Salida stage.

## Dr. O'Rourke Ponders the Badman John Sprockett and the Late Reverend Burden

Sprockett's an enigma,
able to quote more lines
of verse than I can,
but a temper deadly
as a cornered wolverine.
I'd known men like him
back in Galway,
who looted and burned
in the name of Sacred Ireland.

As for Preacher Burden,
he never saw me in the street,
but stopped me — his forefinger
harder than all the cannons
at the Boyne — and warned
I was a damned Papist.

I'd quote Scripture verse,
but he'd fire back
with a chapter of his own;
then I'd spout Gaelic poetry,
to convince him
I spoke in demon-tongues.

I examined his corpse,
smashed up from its fall,
stuck to one fingernail,
a thread of a bandanna:
Sprockett's,
though I don't know why.

My duty's to the living.

## The Widow Burden, the Night After Her Husband's Funeral

If only I could make Mr. Sprockett
confess what transpired between him
and my husband at the abandoned shaft.
But why should I care how or why
my husband left this world,
when he had taken up with a saloon girl?

Because I must solve the evil riddle
Aunt prophesied for my marriage
to a man of unbending Scripture;
Father and I dazzled by the sermons
Thomas spun like an impromptu spider:
Aunt the only one immune to his weaving.

A whisper warns, "You know why he died."
But I want to hear it from Mr. Sprockett,
whom I surprised leaving me a gold pouch
the night my husband disappeared.

That night I clutched the gold, sobbing,
"Is this what love meant to you, Thomas?"
Now, I shudder to think of speaking
to Mr. Sprockett's bear-troweled face,
his scars the least of what I fear
from our interview.

If only I possessed the courage
to ask Mr. Eagle Feather
to accompany me, but no doubt
he considers me only a white woman
who runs in terror
from his beautiful half-breed face.

∾

# The Widow Burden, Three Nights After Her Husband's Funeral

My husband's dead,
yet all I can think of
is William Eagle Feather
and our one encounter
in mountain air
crisp as autumn apples.

Skinning a rabbit,
he smiled politely
at a harmless stranger:
his face, lovely sandstone;
hair black as a racing stallion
in repose; his eyes,
my aunt's rich morning coffee.

I doubt he even saw me
as a woman; he needs a squaw
who can ride bareback,
fire an arrow, thrust a dagger,
and drop child after child.

My dry womb nudged Thomas
toward Mary LaFrance.
I'd have lavished on an infant
the love my husband never
required of me,
once he realized
I couldn't give him a son.

## William Eagle Feather Contemplates
## the Widow Burden

Weeks before her husband's husk
flew down that shaft,
Miz Burden traipsed up
to my mountain camp
with an empty berry pail,
saying the day was so lovely
she forgot to pick
any of the blue nuggets,
wind a tune she had to follow.

I couldn't read in her face —
harder to figure than tracks
in flinty ground — what she wanted.
If it was just a walk,
she'd put herself in danger:
a woman alone as easy pickings
for a grizzly as swiping honey,
or taking a runt fawn for a cougar.

If to shed her Christian skin,
even more parlous for me,
a half-breed: if I was caught
with a minister's wife,
I'd jerk like a locomotive
had took off both my legs.

Still, at her man's funeral
she did flicker a smile at me,
or I thought she did.
Ever since, she's all
I've been able to think of.

The wind's the only company
I ever needed. Now,
its lonesome moaning
drives me to town,
to offer her my condolences.

## The Widow Burden's Suspicions About John Sprockett

When Mr. Sprockett haunted my cottage —
the night my husband never returned —
and left that pouch Chistmased with nuggets,
he refused to say why the gold belonged to me.

Whenever I've thought of his visit,
a scorpion chill creeps into my heart.
For the one offense that badman finds
unforgivable: disrespect to the weaker sex.

Alive, my husband cast amorous eyes —
and more — at Mary LaFrance.
Not a large leap across a narrow chasm
to think Thomas would leave a barren wife:
an abomination to Gold Creek's preacher.

From there, no more than a stride
over a dry stream bed
for him to consider divorce a sin
he could no more countenance
than deny Jesus spoke directly to him.

And from believing
a legal sundering blasphemous,
Thomas had only one course left,
my heart rasping like a rabbit
in one of Mr. Eagle Feather's snares,
to contemplate his dread logic.

## Mary LaFrance Ponders Her Relationship to the Late Reverend Burden

What tickled me about Preacher?
He thought himself pure as Jesus,
but it wasn't me Delilahed
a good man from a life of Gospel.
First time he spied me,
his eyes burned right through
my Kansas City silk dress.

Later, he called me his altar,
like we was wed; he'd whine
his wife didn't know
the ways to please a man I did;
and he couldn't educate her
without giving our game away.

I suspected what he was planning
for her, wanted to tell him
it'd be better if we left,
took new names, like we'd been baptized
and born-again; but someone took care
he'd not succeed. My money's on
John Sprockett, a skillet-hard killer
with a soft spot for the ladies;

not knowing we're all whores
under the faces respectable wives
put on like party masks
they're afraid to set aside.

∽

## The Widow Burden, After Her Second Interview
## with John Sprockett

I thought I could bear the worst
as if I'd only spent an evening
practicing hymns.
But when Mr. Sprockett reluctantly
nodded that yes, my minister husband
had indeed wanted me dead,
the earth crumbled around me.

I fear I insulted Mr. Sprockett,
by not allowing him to bear me up
when I staggered from the treachery.
It wasn't his scar-scratched face
that made me turn away, but his knowing
that for Thomas I was an inconvenience.

I suppose I should feel flattered
Mr. Sprockett considers me a lady,
a saint worthy of poetry.
But all we women really wish for
is to be treated with respect.
If we're quoted verses to as well,
a Christmas window display.

Somehow, I reached the cottage
Thomas and I once shared,
resolved to quit it at once,
but fatigue shackled my arms and legs.
All I could think of:
if only William would hold me,
and say there was one haven
on this earth where I was welcome.

# John Sprockett, After His Second Interview with the Widow Burden

She could've screamed
I'd killed her husband,
disbelieving the Preacher
wanted her dead.
Or she could've shrieked
at my grizzly-scarred face,
uglier than raiding Blackfeet
painted all the colors of war.

But she only thanked me,
grateful I'd saved her
from that small, nasty dog;
my heart pierced by an arrow
sweeter than a honeycomb
dripping more golden
than stream-glitter.

But plain as splashes
on a paint pony, she's sweet
on that breed tracker.
Jealousy rose up in me
like Yellowstone's garden
of hell-geysers and ghosts.

Simple as snapping
a twig, to kill him,
but she'd still never smile
at me like she does on him,
when no one's watching but me.

❧

## Sylvia Williams, Boarding House Owner

Ever since I first run into
that crazy white man, John Sprockett,
he couldn't keep a thing from me
like I was the confiding sister he never had.
He started me in the boarding house trade
after sampling my biscuits and gravy
when he found me wandering like Israelites
after I run off from Master and Missus
and he'd given up killing Kansas folks
that believed in freeing us slaves.

John said he was ashamed of that episode,
but he can't keep himself from killing.
This time, it's Reverend Burden,
who, I admit, used to quote Jesus at me:
"Slaves, obey your masters."
I pointed out to that toad-spit
there wasn't no slaves no more,
and my shotgun — propped under his nose —
could outargue Jesus if He demanded
room and board, but no coins to pay.

John insisted Burden was biding
his time for a midnight exaltation.
"Let me see to him," John spat;
I said no, not wanting that sorry ghost
interfering with my sleep.
Still, John did kill him,
as a kindness to the Preacher's widow.

Should've been Eagle Feather's job:
a blind man can see he'd laugh
at Apache torture
if her fingers were to scissor
his black hair off his face.

Gambler Longstreet's taking bets
on how it happened. I put a dollar on
"Accident." Longstreet chuckled,
"As innocent as God made you black."
I smiled and said, "You may be right."

## Max Longstreet, Gambler, Speculates on the Death of Reverend Burden

I've turned
his unfortunate demise
to profit, taking bets
on whose hand shoved him
from this world.

My pick?
Sheriff Dennehy,
though it makes
no difference to me
who Our Law kills
so long as I run
my honest faro table.

Whenever Widow Burden's
within pissing distance,
he tips his hat, smiles
greasy as a bear
about to make a meal
of a prime doe.

Even that colored
boarding house owner
laid a bet.
"Accident!" she chimed,
simple enough to believe
Burden slipped.

Preacher would've burned
her out, for sure,
if not for her partner,
John Sprockett.

He recites poetry
to her of an evening,
though I doubt
she understands
a word
of his nonsense.

༄

# William Eagle Feather Gives Lavinia Burden a New Name

After she stumbled
into my camp that once,
I tried to forget
she'd sat like an angel by my fire,
her hair gold as sunflowers.
When our eyes locked,
her face turned red as mine.

If I'd spoke my feelings plain
in town, Sheriff would've made
a dancing aspen leaf of me.
But all I could think of
was Widow Burden brushing out
her golden fiddle strands.

So last night I crept up
to her cottage — my heart
pounding like a war drum —
and whispered,
"Hair Filled With Sun,"
her smile bright as daisies
when she took my hand,
and led me to Paradise.

How all this will end
I fear to think,
but even a half-breed
can dream.

∾

## John Sprockett Considers the Widow Burden and William Eagle Feather

They're stuck as molasses,
that's the problem:
her a preacher's widow,
him a half-breed folks tolerate
for being a Shakespeare
at tracking long riders.

He knew I did the Preacher,
and why, but kept silent,
so I owe him.

Still, a lynch mob might pin
Preacher's death on them:
aside from that opera singer
whose voice can sharp-shoot glass,
our one entertainment's
a hanging, and if a woman
does that mortal waltz,
even better,
like that calico-Sally
exalted for blasting
her fancy-man beater.

After the one time
I rode her, she returned
to reading poetry.
I recited one; she sobbed,
"I'll do you free from now on,"
like I was her golden knight.
Neither poetry nor me
could save her,
though I can help Miss Lavinia
and her half-breed sparker:
pay my debt to that whore.

## William Eagle Feather, After a Visit from Chief Many Horses

He's one pure-blood
that don't spit
when I cross his path.
At least the tribes
hate me honest:
don't act
like they're saving
my soul for Jesus.

They've got no future:
whites rounding them up
for reservation-jails,
claim it's an honor
to scratch the soil
and not hunt the buffalo
disappearing like the magic
tricks I seen once,
at a medicine show.

Many Horses knows
I can keep my mouth shut
about his plans
for a ghost-dance battle.
I could almost hear him
chant his death-song.

When he was gone,
I dreamed of
Hair Filled With Sun,
and the night we'd spent,
the nights and days and nights
we might spend,
if folks just leave us alone.

∾

## Sheriff Dennehy Makes His Intentions Plain
## to the Widow Burden

I'm a plain-spoken man, Lavinia,
and a widow out here alone,
has but three choices:
move back to her kin, agree
to the unthinkable, or remarry.
Your family's passed on,
and Miss Jezebel's establishment
ain't for a minister's widow.

Reverend didn't leave you
comfortable, though I'll not soil
his memory, some accusing
he had a wandering eye,
and then some.

I could kneel and spout poetry,
like that murderer Sprockett,
who, I'll bet, knows more
about Reverend's death
than even I could get out of him.
But poetry's not my honest
way of courting.

Like I said, I'm not given
to Shakespeare-speeches,
just to saying
what's in my heart,
and my heart's calling to you.

## Lavinia Burden Replies to Sheriff Dennehy's Proposal of Marriage

Dear Sheriff,
you flatter me greatly,
but my husband's passing
is still too recent and raw
for me to entertain
a second marriage.

I can't say
what my plans are,
the Reverend Burden
leaving me not
quite so secure
as I'd been led
to believe:
which you were kind
enough to point out.
And my family
does reap the rewards
of their righteous lives,
as we all hope to.

Life's so precarious —
witness my late husband's
fall — that I believe
I shall lose my mind
to be deprived again;
and worry for my safety
might distract you
in a situation calling
for your panther reflexes.

Dear Sheriff Dennehy,
were I to enter
the blessed state again,
I'd consider your suit
with all seriousness.
But for now,
I can only offer thanks
for this great honor:
you, Gold Creek's
one indispensable citizen.

## The Widow Burden, After Rejecting Sheriff Dennehy's Suit

My refusal tiptoed through
a nest of rattlesnakes.
He's Sheriff, after all,
and can make my sojourn here
a hell of trumped-up charges.

I fought my gorge when he trod
my plank floor like a buccaneer,
and spat an albatross of tobacco,
before launching his soliloquy.

And when he mentioned
John Sprockett, I feared
he'd discovered that good man
of violence had killed my husband
and given me the pouch
I buried under one floorboard
that creaked my guilt
whenever Sheriff's boot
struck it like a flint.

Oh, to be with William
in the wilderness
and damn the consequences
of forsaking my civilized life,
but at least clear
of this great filthy teat of gold
that prospectors suck at
with the greed of piglets.

## Sheriff Dennehy, After His Rebuffed Proposal

She didn't say "No" outright,
though I'll be damned
if I know what she did say
through all her flattery,
like words was fine whiskey.
She'll come around,
her tiny inheritance'll
run out fast, 'specially
if me and Banker van Gelder
come to an understanding.

I've done it with whores,
with Ute squaws I had to punch
before they'd squirm
feisty as ferrets,
and with that China doll
that cries before,
during, and after;
but something about Lavinia —
hair like an aspen
filled with autumn —
drives me to beg
for a church wedding.

Preacher was a fool
to take up with a hussy;
lucky for me he took
a careless step or got help;
don't matter, 'cept folks
is restless for an exaltation.

When Lavinia says "Yes,"
I'll know the difference
between grizzly-rough
and dove-gentle.

## The Widow Burden, Caught in a Quandary

I pray for a path
through this labyrinth:
whether to tell William
that my heart sings
whenever I close my eyes
and see his face,
speak his name;
or to board the Denver stage,
take the eastbound,
and live on the pouch of gold
Mr. Sprockett gave me:
resigned to my heart
drying up like leaves
in an autumn wind.

The former soars my veins
with terror and delight;
the latter, dull reason:
what life can I expect
with a half-wild man
who haunts the forests,
hates his white side
even more than he does
the Indian, suffering
abuse from both camps?

Last night, while I cried
over Thomas' cruelty
in life and death,
William appeared,
lay beside me, whispered,
"Live wild with me."

"I must think," I moaned,
not sure if he were man
or phantom,
my cold arms not caring.

## William Eagle Feather, Impatient for an Answer

"Wait," she begged me;
but her heart sings
for me, like mine for her.
I've lived too long
with only the company
of the wind
that used to be enough.

Now, there's Lavinia,
a name as hard for me to say
as white men stumble
over the name
my Ute mother gave me.

It's the first step away
that scares
Hair Filled With Sun;
but in this town —
as mad with gold fever
as a frothing fox
with the biting sickness —
there's only gossip
sharp as a lance,
men that'll use her hard
as a lathered pony.

When she poured out
how her husband tried
to have her killed,
I held her; she shook
like she'd break apart.
I'd have butchered
the bastard Apache-slow:
lucky for him
he's already dead.

Life's too short and mean
for her and me to wait.

## The Widow Burden Meets William Eagle Feather
## Outside of Gold Creek

I searched for William's campfire,
seeking a scrap of solace
from the man I can't help loving,
but whose life in the woods
is so strange and wild.

Each tree loomed identical,
each crackling twig a cougar.
Desperate and despairing,
I cast about for the dim path
back to town: vanished
in that dark, magic-wood.

In dusk mist, a great owl
swooped like Thomas' ghost.
"You adulterous hypocrite!"
I shrieked. A rough hand
stifled my mouth, lungs filling
with terror's silent music.

William! I kissed him fierce,
tore at his clothes,
like women who risk all,
in novels.

"Come away with me now,"
he caressed me after
we had dressed again.
I took one step with him,
one back to town — the path
suddenly as clearly marked
as the boulevards
of my Boston girlhood.

❧

## Lavinia Burden Risks Everything

I'd decided life
with William was impossible.
But just as I was packing,
resigned to a Boston widow's
lonely drizzle of years,
William appeared, and led me
into the moonless night.

When my husband had been alive,
that cottage was my prison,
especially when he led "Revelation
Sessions," the only revealing
his and Mary LaFrance's
naked flesh.

Now, with each step away,
I felt William and I could fly.
That night we lit no fires,
shared jerked venison and huddled
in each other's arms, knowing
the Sheriff would lead a posse,
his vanity tormented,
like a wolf caught in a steel trap,
that I'd chosen another.

With the first gray of dawn,
we were off, a biting rain
devouring our footprints
as if swallowed by a tide,
like that childhood holiday
when I danced among Cape Cod
fairy-waves.

No less an elfin maiden now,
soaring to wherever the wind,
and William, might lead me.

❧

## William Eagle Feather Flees Gold Creek
## with the Widow Burden

I crept up to her cottage,
saw her lanterned-silhouette,
packing for a widow's lonely life
Back East, leaving us both empty
as a medicine bag white soldiers spill,
laughing at Ute superstitions.

Panther silent, I stole in;
one look and she was in my arms,
then we were away, her stooping
for a sack under a floorboard.

Safely up the mountain,
she showed me that pouch.
"My husband's ghost," she whispered,
letting wind scatter the gold dust
like his soul that'll never find
the Land of Plentiful Game.

We couldn't stop laughing:
joy pure as spring winds blowing
the last winter snows away.
She kissed me, again and again,
night shimmering in the emerald robes
whites call, "Northern Lights."

We were snug in that hideout:
between kissing and loving,
we ciphered our path away
from her white life, forever.

∾

## Sheriff Dennehy Discovers the Widow Burden Gone

I'd come courting all proper,
with picked mountain flowers,
hair pomaded, the shirt and jacket
I wear for burying town officials.
But when I saw no chimney smoke,
I drew my gun, nudged open her door —
hearth cold as a buzzard-picked carcass,
armoire gaping like a shotgun wound.

But no sign of a struggle,
even I could tell that:
always that half-breed Eagle Feather
to whistle up like my hound,
when we had to hunt a man down.
Him and Lavinia took off together,
the rumors and gossip all true.

She made a fool of me,
her and that half-breed cur
that hated me for snapping
my fingers to make him track
long riders or reservation jumpers.
But he never flung away
the coin or two I'd toss him.

So now my duty's clear:
form a posse and jerk him
to Jesus, for stealing the gal
I'd cut out from the herd.
Her, I'll sell to Miss Jezebel,
forced to do the nasty with me
and every three-fingered prospector
with brimstone breath,
so she won't get tossed out
with the slops, to die in the snow.

☙

## Mary LaFrance, After the
## Widow Burden's Escape

I never thought
she had the gumption
to fly this gold hell-town.
Not with Sheriff Dennehy
ogling her for his bed-slave,
otherwise called "wife."
Couldn't take his eyes
from her hair: more golden
than the dust hill rats kill for.

The lease at the cottage
Reverend rented for me is up,
lucky Judge Samuel fancies me.

Still, if only it was me
Widow's tracker looked at
like Northern Lights spreading
their green satin gowns,
like that night
when Jesus tossed open
the windows of Heaven.

I'd run my fingers
through his breed-black hair,
softer than songbird feathers,
while he kissed me all over.

Instead, I get Judge Sam:
hands slick as skillet grease,
lips a pair of snails
dripping their slime
whenever they crawl over me.

And there's his wife,
who'd take a cleaver to me,
and drag him back home,
tugging on his ear
like a truant schoolboy.

ॐ

## Madam Jezebel LeDoux, After the Widow Burden's Escape

I could've told Dennehy
what Brutus confided:
spying that half-breed
in the Widow's bedroom.

But Brutus warned,
"Let them be," snarling
the way he told me he'd growled
at one overlord too free
with his bullwhip,
forcing women slaves
to service him, and like it.
He met the man after Emancipation,
snapped his neck like a chicken.

But if I'd told Dennehy —
slick at murdering witnesses
and taking bribes —
we could've made sure
the Widow didn't run.

It burns my liver:
the business I'd've done
with a slack puller legally
poked by a man of God,
even one as flawed
as her husband'd been.

But the barbed wire in Brutus' eyes
was like nothing I'd ever seen,
not even when he beats
white hill rats
who mistreat our girls.

## Brutus Hawkins, Bouncer, Speaks of the Widow Burden

If Jezebel'd insisted
I kidnap the Widow,
we'd've had our first argument.
She mentioned it once;
miners, she declared.
crazy for a preacher's angel.

Much as I admire Jezzy's brains,
and her talent in our four-poster,
I couldn't bear to think
of anyone suffering slavery.
I recalled Libbie
from the slave days,
dragged back after she ran.

I hid behind Mama's skirt,
but a house servant
made me watch;
Libbie's back raw
as a fresh-slaughtered sow,
her shrieks filling the yard
like Satan's church bell.

When Jezzy proposed
we kidnap the Widow,
I put one big hand
over her mouth, real gentle;
then we did what we do best,
no more talk of forcing
whoring, slave ways on anyone.

## Sheriff Dennehy Recruits a Posse from Those Drinking in His Saloon

"Up, you drunken
hill rats, you spawn
of thirst-parlor sluts.
That dirty half-breed
stole off with the Widow Burden,
forced her at knife-point,
the filthy, raping son
of a feeble-minded squaw.

"Up, or I'll shoot
every goddamn man here,
and them I don't plug,
will buck and wing
with a hemp bandanna
round their throats.

"We ride to save
a pure-white angel.
But if I find she ran
of her own accord,
every man gets a turn
with the breed-loving whore.

"Then it's not just a case
of a spun-gold hussy
flying off
with that smudged demon,
but of her husband's murder:
only a matter of time
before I find the proof.

"Up, you pus-suckers.
I count to five,
then I start shooting!"

❧

# Francis DeLacey Rides in the Posse After the Widow Burden and William Eagle Feather

I didn't need Isaac Newton
to figure we'd never find
that half-breed tracker,
even with him hauling Widow Burden.
I was just hoping to nose out
who killed her preacher husband:
that tracker no more a murderer
than Pinhead Jones can string
two words that make sense.

What we mostly did was drink:
boys spinning in their saddles
like they were riding mustangs
more snake blooded than twisters.
After a week, I dreamed
of hot baths and spicy whores;
but Sheriff still in a grizzly rage:
the tracker besting him
for a woman skinny as a pick-axe;
no accounting for men's tastes
when they're love-blind.

Speaking of grizzlies,
that bear-ripped wall of thunder,
John Sprockett, was our one
sensible vigilante: announcing
our fool's errand over;
and God help anyone disagreeing
with that short trigger
hell-fiend.

If only Sprockett'll help me
sniff out the real killer.

### Sheriff Dennehy, Once the Posse Returns

One thing for Preacher
to've pranced around
with Mary LaFrance.
A man's got needs.

But for his widow to vanish
with the breed tracker
and ignore my marriage proposal,
that's going against your own,
and a mortal insult!

So I whipped the boys up
to such a lather
they'd have jerked
the first stranger
our posse came across.

But up rides Sprockett,
swearing he can read signs
good as that breed,
and who's going to tell him
he can't, a man who can murder
quicker than most can sneeze?

We spent a week riding hard,
sleeping on harder ground,
vittles running out,
liquor running dry
as drought-parched streams.

Finally, we turned back.
You ask me, what Sprockett
angled for all along.
Maybe he helped
send Preacher to Paradise,
but I ain't dumb enough
to say so.

## John Sprockett, After the Posse Returns

I led Dennehy's drunk posse
in circles and onto false trails;
around ghostly campfires I told
of Utes drooling to sink arrows
and knives into white men's guts.

Between my terror tales
and the liquor getting drunk up,
they had less stomach to search
than General Lee to continue
the War he knew we'd lose
before he gathered an army.

Sheriff knows I'll kill him
quicker than I'd swat a fly
if he asks me how that snake
of a minister got found
at the Hell-end of a dry shaft.

Let the Widow and her Tracker
find a long happy life together,
far from where I might be forced
to keep their mouths shut forever.

❧

## Mary LaFrance Watches the Posse Return

A half-breed out-footed
mounted men, and him slowed
by the Preacher's Widow.
To trap him would've took
a woman using herself as bait:
but no one asked my opinion
about men sticking their necks
into nooses for love.

The posse would've enjoyed him
puppet-dancing from a rope,
then taking turns on her;
but tracking? Too much work.

Sheriff whipped them on —
braying like a wounded mule
to find the Widow missing —
but she'd rather have pulled slack
with a rattler than with him:
and the breed's a fine-looking man.

Now, the posse's pouring
into Sheriff's saloon,
bragging about almost catching,
"The mongrel and his white slut."
But Sprockett smashes his bottle,
and they fall silent, him hating
when any woman's spoken of
like tossed away apple cores;
still, he gives me the creeps
like a spider was grave-dancing
down my face.

I'll have to explain
my belly bump to Judge Sam;
him and me did go a round
or two on them nights
Tommy got stuck with his wife.
Judge Sam'll think himself
a hero to have planted me proper.

❧

## William Eagle Feather Hears of the Death of John Sprockett, 1876

We always feared he'd repent
of saving us: first,
from her husband,
then from the posse
that would've hung us,
since someone had to pay
for the crow-coat's death.

Now, we can breathe easy,
though I grieve the man,
his soul troubled as rivers
raging down from the peaks.
He was a thunder-god of death
filled with scorpion juice.

The wind-imp hisses
a woman stole his soul
when she returned
to her own people,
and he allowed himself
to be gunned down from ambush.
I can't think any woman
delighted in his scarred face.
But Hair Filled With Sun laughs,
"Scars disappear to eyes in love."

Maybe he'll meet that thief-woman
in the Land of Plentiful Game,
will forgive her for pouring
ashes onto his heart; and they —
like Hair Filled With Sun and me —
will dance in the mountains forever.

## William Eagle Feather Changes His Name

When I gave you the name
Hair Filled With Sun,
you smiled, wore it
more gracefully
than Mrs. Lavinia Burden.

Now, it's time for me
to pick a new name:
Finds the Path,
a name that counts coup
over the white blood
that battles inside me
with the Ute.

Your eyes glitter mischief,
thinking this new name
a vanity
when I should be finding us
a good berry patch,
or if the smoke
you spy in the distance
is a white settlement
or some escaped Lakotas:
even more dangerous
for us to get close to.

But I do find the paths
we follow
in our mountain dodging
of desperate bands,
and of settlers and soldiers
howling vengeance
for Custer.

If half the rumors
whispered of him be true,
an unholy fool.

# Hair Filled With Sun: the Colorado Rockies, Late 19th Century

When we escaped Gold Creek
for a life of wilderness wandering,
I cried at first: for my bed,
a bath, clean fingernails,
but soon saw them as fripperies.

The first time I snared a rabbit,
I clapped hands with the joy
of a girl mastering ice skates.
When I learned to make fire
from twigs, dry leaves,
and my inspiring breath,
I watched, rapt as God —
forgive my blasphemy —
calling the sun into existence.

Soon, I could sniff out deer,
the rank brutality of bears,
could brazen wolves
from their kills.
We never attempted those thefts
on wolverines: more fierce
than any creature save Mr. Sprockett,
God rest the troubled angel
of his soul.

Soon, I could find
a trail or bushwhack one
through what a white man
would deem impassable brush.
The years have sped by
in our delight and hard work.

And soon, so very soon —
my aching bones
and rasping breaths inform me —
I must tread the trail that ends,
I pray, in mountains untouched
by toadstools of white settlements.

May we walk to that Good Land
like trusting children, hand in hand.

❧

## Finds the Path Mourns

Hair Filled With Sun died today.
I hoisted her into a tree,
so she can fly off easy
to the Land of Plentiful Game.

Sometimes, when she thought
I wasn't looking, she'd sigh
for a bath or a new dress,
or her Boston childhood,
or even that gold hell-town
I took her from.

Still, she swore she wouldn't
trade our wandering for anything.
Then she'd hold me tight
and sing she loved me more
than her own breath
or the kids she couldn't have.

Hair Filled With Sun,
I named her. She said
I was a natural poet;
she took to snaring game
like she'd been a fox
before she was a woman,
could stitch our leggings
and tunics finer
than a Lakota squaw.

Just let me see her again:
in her preacher Pa's heaven,
or my poor Ute Mother's
Land of Plentiful Game,
or in Hell, but together;
even if we're old
and wrinkled and useless,
except to each other.

∾